Someday We'll Play in Heaven

Shawn Alyne Strannigan

illustrated by Dorothy Donohue

The Standard Publishing Company, Cincinnati, Ohio
A division of Standex International Corporation

Printed in the United States of America
02 01 00 99 98 97 96 95 5 4 3 2 1
Designed by Coleen Davis

Cataloging-in-Publication data available
ISBN 0-7847-0290-X

Helping Young Children Grieve

For very young children, death is an abstract that can be grasped only a little at a time. As this book illustrates, it took Lindsay a full year to accept the permanence of her brother Jonah's death. Keeping that fact in mind, here are some suggestions to help ease your child through the loss of a loved one.

Tell the truth, but gently.
If your child isn't given an adequate explanation when death occurs, he may fill in the blanks with fantasy. And a child's imaginings will usually be more frightening than the truth. Avoid euphemisms such as "He passed away" or "She's just sleeping," which will only confuse your child and prolong denial. Explain to your child what will take place at the funeral, and if he's willing, allow him to attend with you.

Create an open atmosphere in your home.
Share your own feelings of loss with your child and encourage him to do the same. Invite your child to ask questions, and be honest with your answers.

Watch for signs of distress.
Children go through the same stages of grief as adults — shock, denial, anger, bargaining, and acceptance. But children can get stuck in denial trying to protect themselves from pain. Symptoms of distress include behavior changes such as tantrums, bed-wetting, and nightmares. If your child appears to be having trouble working through his grief, Christian counseling may help.

Pour on the love.
Parents can become so wrapped up in their own emotions that their children feel abandoned. Take time to reach out to your child and reassure him or her of your love.

— *SAS*

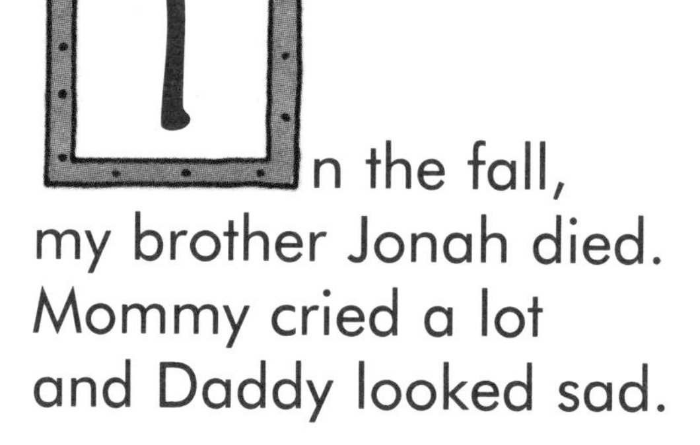

In the fall,
my brother Jonah died.
Mommy cried a lot
and Daddy looked sad.

ommy, why are you crying?

Because I loved Jonah, honey,
and I miss him so much.

I miss him, too, Mommy.

I know.

In the winter,
Jonah's birthday came.
He would have been five,
so Mommy made a cake
with five candles.

Will Jonah come to his birthday party?
Oh, Daddy, will he stay?

No, dear, Jonah lives in heaven now.

But we sang to him anyway.

Happy Birthday
Jonah
HOLY BIB

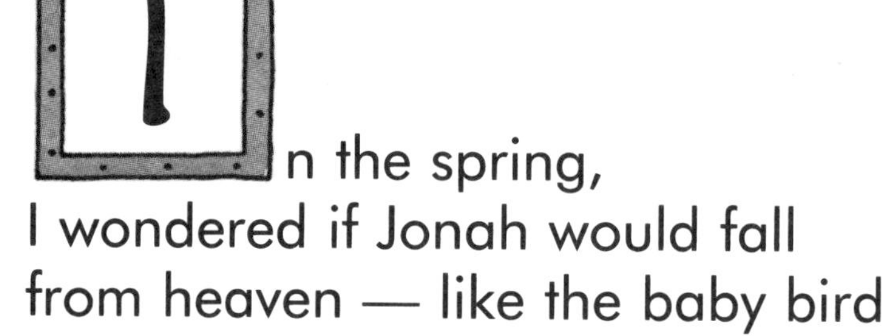

In the spring,
I wondered if Jonah would fall
from heaven — like the baby bird
that fell out of a tree into our yard.

fed Birdie every day, but he died.

Why are you crying, Lindsay?

Because I loved my bird, Mommy,
and I miss him so much.

I know, honey. I miss Birdie, too.
It hurts to lose something you love.

In the summer,
I got a kitten —
and a new baby sister!
Mommy smiled a lot,
and Daddy pushed me on the swing.

One day we took flowers to Jonah's grave.

No, Sissy, we won't *see* Jonah today, because he lives in heaven now, with Jesus . . .

BIBLE

But someday,
we'll play with him in heaven!

My Memories Pages

Lindsay keeps a picture of Jonah by her bed. Ask your mom or dad for some pictures of the person you want to remember. Cut them to fit the frames on this page and then glue them in place. If you like, you can draw your own picture of your special person in one of the frames instead.

My Memories Pages

When Jonah died, sometimes Lindsay felt very sad. But sometimes she smiled when she remembered the fun things they had done together, like chasing the waves at the beach and climbing trees. Lindsay also liked to think about Jonah's favorites things — pinwheels and Bugs Bunny.

If someone you love has died, remembering special things and special times together can help you feel better, too. Fill in the blanks with the name of your loved one. Then draw pictures or ask someone older to help you write what you want to remember.

Special times I had with ______________

______________'s favorite things

The stories in this series are based on events experienced by the author and her family. They would be glad to hear from children who are coping with the loss of a loved one. Children too young to write a letter might want to draw a picture. Be sure to include a return address.
To send a letter or a picture, write:
Shawn Strannigan
c/o Standard Publishing
Children's Book Department
8121 Hamilton Avenue
Cincinnati, OH 45231